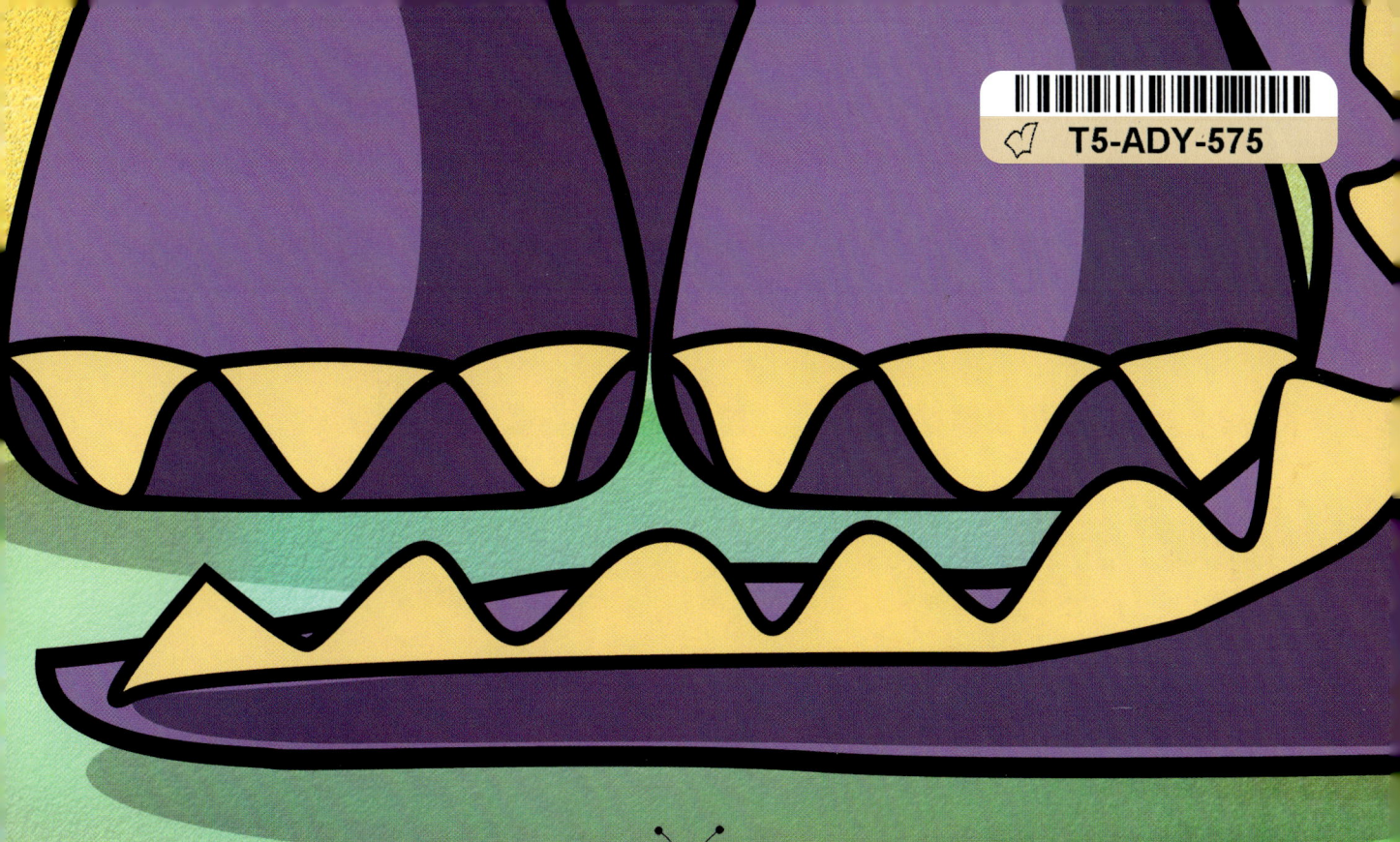

Those with **big feet** or small stubby toes.
Those who hear laughter for wearing wrong clothes.

Those who are **clumsy**,
who can't kick the ball.

In case you are wondering,
this book is for **all**.

For we all have times
when we feel less.

When our shirt sticks out funny
and our **hair** is a **mess**.

I am a **Stuffie**, I know where true **greatness** sprouts. For I see the world from the **inside** out.

Inside of us all
we carry life's **treasure.**

Like friendship and **love**,
the stuff great lives
are measured.

Inside of me are treasures to **hold**.
Not silver, not diamonds,
not bright shiny gold.

But all of the things that matter to you.

Like the yo-yo your Grandpa gave you at two.

The baseball your big brother finally passed down.

Or the dolly Grandma got from the big store uptown.

If it's important to YOU,
it's important to ME.

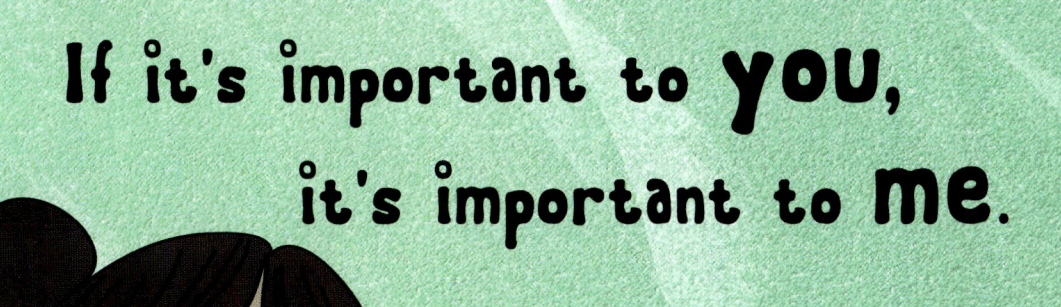

For Stuffies know value
lies beyond what you see.

We protect with a roar, a bark or a pounce.

Because all Stuffies know...

Manners   Imagination

It's what's inside that counts!

Knowledge

Courage

Sharing

Love

Friendship

7 Secret Pockets!

secret pockets

travel buddy

cozy pillow

perfect gift

Stuffies™

It's what's inside that counts!™

Stuffies™

It's what's inside that counts!™